TIMOTHY, TITUS & YOU

A Workbook for Church Leaders

—REVISED EDITION—

GEORGE C. SCIPIONE

TIMELESS TEXTS
WOODRUFF, SC

To the elders of Calvary Community Church
Allan, Ben, Peter, Mark, Allen, Bud and Dick
and to their faithful example,
Lew

Thanks go to my wife, Eileen, and to Jay E. Adams.
Their help on the manuscript and overall encouragement
have been invaluable.

Above all,
praise goes to Jesus Christ,
the Great Shepherd of the sheep,
for encouraging me through His Spirit.

CONTENTS

FOREWORD
to the Revised Edition

Several years ago, I walked into a dusty little antiquarian book-shop in New York and providentially discovered a frayed, foxed, and frazzled copy of a booklet entitled *Heed the Call*. It had been written for a now practically-forgotten ecclesiastical crisis in 1844 by Thomas Chalmers. A great Scottish pastor, social reformer, educator, author, and scientist, Chalmers lived from 1780 to 1847. During the course of his long and storied career, he served as the pastor of three congregations, taught in three colleges, published more than thirty-five best-selling books, and helped to establish more than a hundred charitable relief and missions organizations. He practically reinvented the Scottish parish system as well as the national social welfare structure. He counted such luminaries as the Duke of Wellington, Sir Walter Scott, King William IV, Thomas Carlyle, William Wilberforce, and Robert Peel as his friends and confidantes. Indeed, he was among the most influential and highly regarded men of his day. Even so, at the end of his life, when his reputation was well-established, his contribution to the life of Scotland, England and Ireland fully recognized, and his fame spread around the world, he did not hesitate to involve himself in—and ultimately lead—a movement that was to divide the Church of Scotland, and to set him in apparent disregard of the authority of the highest civil court in the land.

With the disappearance of Roman Catholic authority in Scotland in the sixteenth century, Reformers worked hard to replace it with a faithful national Church. Their struggle for spiritual independence had been a long and costly one under the leadership of John Knox, Andrew Melville and Alexander Henderson, amongst others. At long last, in 1690, their Reformed Church was legally recognized by the crown as the established Church of Scotland. The danger of such an establish-ment was that the state might attempt to manipulate the internal affairs of the Church.

Sadly, that danger was realized when Parliament imposed conformity with the standards of English patronage upon the Scottish Church. In reality, patronage was hardly different from the Medieval practice of lay investiture—it gave lords, lairds, and landowners the right to appoint to a parish a minister who might or might not be Biblically qualified for the post or acceptable to the elders of the congregation. The patronage conflict came to a head in 1838, when several ministers were forced on congregations opposed to their settlement and the Court of Session and the House of Lords ratified the appointments. Many, including Chalmers, believed that the integrity of the Gospel was at stake.

At about the same time, it was decided by Parliament that the Church did not have the power to organize new parishes nor give the ministers there the status of clergy of the Church. She had no authority to receive again clergy who had left it. And perhaps worst of all, a creeping liberal formalism was slowly smothering the evangelical zeal of the whole land—in large part due to the assumption of the duties of eldership by men altogether unfit for such a solemn vocation.

In other words, there arose in the land a crisis over the issue of what constituted a legitimate call to the eldership, how it was to be recognized, and how it was to be maintained.

Alas, despite repeated requests, the Government refused to take action to deal with the threat of spiritual atrophy that a deficient or subjective view of calling inevitably produced. After a ten year long struggle to regain the soul of the church, the evangelical wing, led by Chalmers and others, laid a protest on the table of the Assembly and some four hundred ministers and a like number of elders left the established Church of Scotland on May 18, 1843, to form the Free Church. When the General Assembly of the Free Church was constituted that grave morning, Thomas Chalmers was called to be its Moderator. He was the man whose reputation in the Christian world was the highest; he was also the man whose influence in directing the events leading to what would eventually be called "The Disruption" had been greatest.

Obviously, if the conflict had been provoked by a faulty view of what actually constituted a call to the ministry of the local church, it was incumbent upon the evangelical leaders to articulate the correct view. Chalmers wrote *Heed the Call* to do just that.

He argued that there were essentially "only two guiding principles for the affirmation of any doctrinal standard, yet which are of particular relevance to the current discussion. They are but the plenary objectivity of Holy Writ and the living appurtenance of parish life; again, they are but the authority of Scripture and the parameters of the covenant." In other words, he believed that it was not necessary to depend on either the predilections of the rich and powerful or the inclinations of the people at large to determine who was or who wasn't called into the ministry. The Bible was, is, and always shall be clear in detailing specific criteria and prerequisites for vocational service in the Church. But not only that, covenantal communities serve as the proving grounds for those criteria and prerequisites so that there is a kind of checks and balances system at work.

Chalmers asserted that the Bible makes it plain that any candidate for the ministry as well as the members of his immediate family must evidence constancy of character and virtue over the course of time (I Tim. 3:1-7; Titus 1:5-9). He must also demonstrate particular pastoral gifts and aptitudes in the handling of the Gospel (Eph. 4:4-16; II Tim. 2:15-16). As he said, "The Word of God countenances as requisite both a testable sanctification and a notable endowment." And such mandatory capacities are observable within the context of everyday parish life (Philem. 4-7). He said, "An affirmation of the ministerial calling is the inevitable result of a life rightly lived, gifts rightly shared, and proficiencies in handling both Scripture and adversity amongst those who might best be able to judge a candidate's sincerity: his neighbors." Accountability is thus assured. He believed that by holding candidates for the eldership ministry to this twin standard, both "the integrity of the Church's divine offices" and the "vitality of every other calling to which believer priests might be appropriately inclined" would be preserved. The result was that mere desire, or opportunity, or inclination, professional preparation, or even obvious aptitude alone was insufficient to commend a man to the pulpit. And despite the need for faithful pastoral servants, all manner of haste in discerning the authenticity of calling was carefully avoided (I Tim. 5:22). Ministry was thus maintained as a vital organism rather than as a mere organization. The Biblical precepts set the standard and then the community of faith affirmed and confirmed compliance with that standard in the life and work of every candidate.

When I first read the almost too-simple prescriptives of Chalmers in *Heed the Call*, I was flooded with a sense of relief. The issue was not nearly as complicated as I had made it out to be. I was able to rest in the assurance that there was no mystical override, no metaphysical trump, no divine notary that I had somehow overlooked or misread.

At the same time, I wondered how and where local churches in our own time might be afforded with this kind of wise counsel—and perhaps even more important, where they might be afforded the kind of substantive training necessary to uphold it. I believe this remarkable workbook you are now reading is the answer.

Like Chalmers before him, George Scipione relies on the clear mandates of Scripture as confirmed by those God has providentially placed around prospective elders in their own local churches. He has reaffirmed the great dictum of Chalmers, "Word and covenant: the one true foundation with its one true environ; they surely are the only, yet fully sufficient, provisions at our disposal for the discernment of purpose in this poor fallen world by which we might duly heed the call." But he has done it in a practical, accessible, and forthright fashion.

This is a book every church ought to utilize as they seek to raise up authentically Biblical elders. It is a book every elder will want to work through again and again throughout his ministry. Indeed, it is the sequel that the work of Chalmers has long needed.

George Grant
Professor of Moral Philosophy
Bannockburn College

FOREWORD
to the First Edition

My good friend and colleague in counseling, George Scipione, has written a readable, practical, valuable and unique volume. I know of nothing else like it. Pastors, elders and the members of their congregations will profit immeasurably from its use. I commend it to you.

Timothy, Titus and You is not simply another study of the eldership; not to say that *that* would be bad. Such studies do not abound. But some do exist. They have their place, and it is a needed one. Indeed, more definitive studies of the many disputed issues pertaining to the eldership, dealing with these problems from a solid exegetical base, are desperately needed. But this volume is unique; it is in no sense whatever "another." It stands alone.

What makes this book unique is that Mr. Scipione allows the Scriptures themselves to speak to the reader with power. Thus, the emphases, the nuances, and the total scriptural impact concerning the qualifications of the elder are preserved.

The book is designed to be used by a pastor, by an elder, or by a group of elders as a study guide. As a tool for training elders, the volume is without parallel and meets a need, long recognized, but never satisfied. The work is set up in units that may be used in a course that extends over a period of months. As each unit's work is devoted to substantive matters, and as personal self-evaluation requiring time and remedial effort will be the outcome of much of this work, it is not advisable to attempt to double up on any of the lessons. The book taken as a whole is formidable; it therefore must be taken in small portions.

Timothy, Titus, and You was not written for persons who are looking for easy answers, tricks, or gimmicks. Recognizing that the effectiveness of elders grows from meaningful confrontation with God in the Scriptures, the author seeks to bring about that confrontation at every point. This is not a book of recipes; to study it through is an *experience.* It is a book for those who want to be examined, rebuked, changed, and stretched. It is easy enough to understand, but hard to take. Christians of every sort, not merely pastors and elders, may profit from the study of this volume. There is much for those of all ages and maturity. Buy it, give it away, use it—to the blessing and benefit of the whole Church of Jesus Christ.

Jay E. Adams
Westminster Theological Seminary
Chestnut Hill, Pennsylvania
March, 1975

PREFACE
to the Third Printing

Don Ritsman, a minister of the Orthodox Presbyterian Church, expresses the most often mentioned criticism of *Timothy, Titus, and You:* "The major criticism I would make is that I found it to be far too much material for a person, especially a layman, to assimilate in a meaningful way. My reaction was that if a sincere, enthusiastic elder was confronted with this total wealth of material he might become overly discouraged. We must be careful not to snuff out a flickering flame by heaping too much fuel upon the fire."

My prayer is that this will never happen! Three things may help to prevent such discouragement.

First, *Timothy, Titus and You* cannot be completed in one month, nine months, or a lifetime. You must grow constantly as a Christian and a church leader. This workbook, Lord willing, should help you *start* growing as a leader and help you *to continue* to grow as you periodically review your work. You can go back over it again and again to check your growth. Thinking that you will have "arrived" in nine months may result in your taking a mechanical, academic approach to the lessons which could lead to frustration if lessons are not completed. Keep in mind that the book is addressed to a living, open-ended situation and not to a closed, static, theoretical one. The workbook is a tool to help you grow in your office, not a magic wand to perfect you all at once.

Second, flexibility is a key to using this study guide. While *Timothy, Titus, and You* is highly structured, you must adapt it to your situation. Because your situation, culture, or subculture is different from mine, you may have to adjust the study. The only part that would not change is the KNOWLEDGE OF THE WORD sections because God's word never changes.

Third, an open, prayerful, and loving relationship among the congregation's leaders is essential. If you have this, the Christian encouragement and exhortation needed to grow in grace will act as a foundation for this study. Otherwise, it will become a mere academic exercise devoid of spiritual life and vigor. You are a real person and need God's people to grow.

We live in challenging times. More than ever before, local congregations need leaders worthy of their calling. Only intense wrestling with God's Word under the Spirit's guidance will accomplish this. May our God bless you in your labors for His Son Jesus Christ, and use this workbook to help you stand with Timothy, Titus and the elders of all ages. "Let us not lose heart in doing good, for in due time we shall reap if we do not grow weary." Galatians 6:9.

G.C.S., 1976

INTRODUCTION

Why a Workbook?

Much discouragement is the result of ignorance. It is a terrible experience to find yourself in a job for which you were not totally prepared. Once that happens, some begin to worry; others give up. When you do not know what you are supposed to do, you may finally despair and get nothing done. If you can't see the mark, you won't hit it; your aim wavers and you lose heart. If you find yourself in a position of leadership, the problem is magnified.

After I graduated from seminary, I was elected to the office of ruling elder in a congregation. Viewing this as God's call to the ministry, I prayerfully accepted. Over several months as an elder-elect, I received training that consisted of reading materials, some discussion of the work, and observation of pastoral calls. Yet in spite of this and my seminary training, I was ill-prepared to lead a congregation. Why? In addition to my sinfulness, I had two problems. Let me tell you about them.

First, I had not wrestled concretely with the biblical data concerning the office. Sure, I had read the Word and prayed about it, but I had not placed myself under the Scriptures as one puts small print under a magnifying glass. It is one thing to read the Word, but it is quite another to *use* it in a practical way.

Second, I had never done the work of an elder, nor even taken much leadership in a local congregation. I had little practice at instructing others in a teacher-disciple relationship, which is the biblical method of teaching. In short, I had not concretely, practically or consciously worked at developing the gifts for the office. While I desired the office under Paul's encouragement in I Timothy 3:1 to do so, I had not adequately prepared for it. I did not have enough knowledge of the Bible or myself, nor did I have enough biblical wisdom in discipling myself or others. Thus, I wandered about more like a sheep than a shepherd.

In talking with other elders, including those elected with me and those in my first pastorate, I have found that many of them have experienced similar problems in regard to their God-given office. Most of them really do want to shepherd the sheep, but do not know how, except in a vague general way. They feel ill-prepared and hopelessly confused. They make attempts, but fail. They try to change, but don't know how. Finally, they throw up their hands and say, "Let the clergy do it!" Yet God, in the Bible, plainly defines the duties of an elder. The Scriptures are sufficient to equip the man of God (II Tim. 3:16-17) for his work as an elder. The pastoral epistles to Timothy and Titus, in particular, give abundant guidance. Therefore, we shall study this God-revealed material in this workbook, but not abstractly. I hope these brief studies will help many elders to see the practical, personal, down-to-earth way in which Paul deals with the office. At the very least, they may point elders back to the Bible for the answers to some of their heartfelt questions.

Who Should Use the Workbook?

Primarily, "men of God" (i.e., elders) may profit from this guide. It also may be used with young men who show potential as elders. Two groups, then, should find it helpful: men seeking the office and men already in the office. Since the workbook was written primarily for those already in office, some of the assignments may have to be altered slightly for use with the first of the two groups, e.g., recommended discussions among the elders may take place in the study group of prospective elders; discussions could be carried on with a wife, a fiancee, or a close male friend; pastoral visitations might be replaced by fellowship times with Christian friends or visits with sick friends.

The pastoral epistles were written in order to encourage and train two ordained elders, Timothy and Titus. Lord willing, this guide may help that encouragement to reach others as they wrestle with the biblical knowledge concerning the office of elder. As we see our sins and failures, we can confess and correct them; only then will we grow. The guide should help those who use it prayerfully to apply biblical discipling to their own lives and to the discipling of others.

Two of my assumptions should be mentioned. First, I assume (without arguing it) that the Presbyterian form of government is the biblical pattern. This means that the guide moves within a given framework. However, an Episcopalian or an Independent may find that, with some adjustments, the guide is useful within his ecclesiastical framework. Second, I assume that there are only two offices in the Body of Christ (elder and deacon), not three (bishop, minister, deacon/minister, elder, deacon etc.). I do not argue for these assumptions since others have done so and since they are not within the scope of this introduction.

While elders and prospective elders clearly are my principal targets, other Christian leaders such as youth directors, Sunday School teachers, Christian School teachers, Boy's Brigade leaders, etc., may profit from the guide. The principles of Christian teaching and management are basically the same in all of these situations. Such leaders may gain fresh insight from a study of the highest office of leadership in the Body of Christ today. Again, by adjusting certain assignments, a leader may make the guide usable for these people and himself.

Finally, all Christians may profit from using the study guide in two ways. First, every Christian has a responsibility in electing those elders who will rule over him. The guide, therefore, may help the church at large to better understand the office of elder and especially to recognize men who are qualified for that office. Reflection of the sort suggested in the workbook will help the church to elect Spirit-filled and Spirit-gifted leaders, rather than the popular men who are leaders in vocational areas alone. Second, every Christian has *some* leadership responsibilities. Parents must lead in the home. Even single people, as priests before God, are responsible to lead themselves. All of us must disciple one another. The guide aims to help people apply these Scriptures to themselves and thus grow in grace and leadership abilities.

How to Use the Study Guide

The method of the nine lessons that follow is uniform. Each lesson is based on a passage of Scripture,[1] but other similar passages should be read along with it.

---

[1] The text used throughout is that of *The Christian Counselor's New Testament*, TIMELESS TEXTS, (Woodruff, SC).

Lesson Goals

Your *first* goal is to gain knowledge of God's Word. There are study questions on each primary Scripture passage. These are personalized so that the Scriptures may confront you individually. Prayerfully study the passage (using the margin to record your answers to the questions). Study the other passages, developing your own questions using the pattern given.

Your *second* goal is to gain knowledge of yourself. Questions and assignments are given so that you may evaluate your eldership (leadership, etc.). Without prayerful honesty and effort here, you will not benefit from the study.

Your *third* goal is to discipline yourself for biblical change. Once you discover your sins, failures and inadequacies, you will be ready to grow by God's grace. This must be followed up by biblically directed action. Faith without works is dead. The assignments given are intended to help you to become a better elder (leader, etc.). Biblical faith includes true repentance or change. The assignments aim at this kind of change.

Your *fourth* goal is to share your growth with others. By sharing, you can help your congregation and others to mature into the image of Jesus Christ. The scope of the study is not limited to the user. God willing, others will be touched and changed as a result of your prayerful use of the workbook. Their prayer and Bible study could be revitalized. Others could be discipled into a fuller walk with our Lord as a result of your study. Whole congregations could be stirred up; this is my prayer. Ultimately, the purpose of this workbook is the building up of the Body of Christ and the glory of its Head, the Lord Jesus Christ.

Use of the Lessons

The workbook is designed for use over a nine month period, one lesson each month. While individual lessons may be studied separately, tne design of the workbook is to study *all* of the material in the pastoral epistles. When these studies were first used, in the embryonic state, it became clear that there was too much to be done in a short span of time. Experience has shown that one lesson a month is a reasonable pace. The course may be used from September to May over the typical American school year. This enables you to avoid vacations and follow the course straight through. At Calvary Community Church, the elders meet during prayer meeting once a month. This avoids an extra meeting night and has fostered unity among the elders. The sections *Knowledge of the Word* and *Knowledge of Self* can be studied as a part of your daily personal worship.[1] Since the Scriptures are being studied and applied to your own heart, it is legitimate to substitute this study for other Bible study, thus avoiding any additional time requirement. It is good to take extra time, but not if this makes your week too busy. This is an important consideration, since improper scheduling can lead to incomplete lessons. Some of the assignments in *Wisdom in Self-Discipling* and *Wisdom in Discipling Others* can be scheduled for use during other meetings in order to save time, thus minimizing the likelihood of incomplete or sloppy assignments.

Caution has been exercised to ensure proper biblical discussion. A biblically oriented, Spirit-filled group of individuals should be able to avoid sinful sensationalism on the one hand and pietistic privacy on the other. Intimate details about your marriage or personal life ought not to be discussed. Our age is a time of total nakedness. Openness is the byword. Total openness cannot be equated with honesty. However, sharing your daily faith and experience of God's work in your life is a *must* for Christian fellowship and growth. I believe the assignments are within proper biblical guidelines.

Perhaps you will wish to improve upon these lessons. Possibly they do not go far enough for you. If this happens, do change them to suit your needs. As long as this guide is used in some way to build up Christ's Body, praise Him! The only area which cannot be tampered with is the Scripture's questions to you.

One final word concerning the use of the workbook: a lot of time went into developing this. The original language was examined before the study questions were formulated; I hope this will help you understand what the text is asking you. Prayerful consideration was given to

---

[1] Fill in the blanks as you study. Then bring this book to group meetings in order to discuss matters together and glean help from others' work.

personalize the questions because the living God is speaking to you. You will find, as I have in *using* this guide, that it does require a lot of time and honest, consistent effort. It is not an easy workbook to use; it was not intended to be. This is a tool for growth as a leader in the Lamb's army. Christian growth or sanctification is never easy, whether on the individual or corporate level; however, it is worth every ounce of energy (cf. I Tim. 4:7-8). You need discipline to profit from this study. Doing the job of an elder correctly is difficult and takes discipline. At times, the job may seem lonely and thankless, requiring more than you have to give. Often this is true, humanly speaking.

Who is sufficient for these things? Not you; not me! However, we *do* have the Bible, which gives us the knowledge of God's will and the knowledge of our failure to measure up to it. Not only do we have God's Word, but I Corinthians 10:13 *is* in the Scriptures! Read *Christ and Your Problems,* J. Adams, (Phillipsburg: Presbyterian and Reformed Publishing Co., 1972). The promises of this verse apply to you as an elder, but the Scriptures not only give knowledge of God's will and your sin, they also help you to become wise in doing God's will. They contain the wisdom that you need to help others. Moreover, Romans 8:14 says that the Holy Spirit will guide you and give you power to do these things. You can, you *must*, shepherd God's flock *by His grace!* God has called you, challenged you and charged you to shepherd His flock.

Also, remember that Jesus Christ is the one perfect Shepherd. When sinful men failed to shepherd God's people (Ez. 34:1-6), He promised to do so personally (Ps. 23; 80:1; Is. 40:1-11; Ez. 34:11-16, 23; Micah 5:1-6). Jesus is the Good Shepherd who lays down His life for the sheep (John 10:11-18). He alone is the Perfect One. You shepherd God's flock by faith. Even though sometimes you may fail, if you partake of the sufferings of Christ you will also possess His glory. Read I Peter 5:1-4; rejoice and reach for the unfading crown of glory. Remember He died to save you and called you to be an elder. Remember He died for all your sins, even those committed *as an elder.* May God revive His under-shepherds and thus revive the whole Body of Christ—beginning with you. Remember Christ's shepherdly love for you; that will help you to love His sheep. May the apostolic benediction of Hebrews 13:20-21 rest upon all those who love the Lord Jesus Christ and use this workbook in faith.

> Now the God of peace, who brought up from the dead the great Shepherd of the sheep through the blood of the eternal covenant, even Jesus our Lord, equip you in every good thing to do His will, working in us that which is pleasing in His sight, through Jesus Christ, to whom be the glory forever and ever, Amen.

G.C.S., 1975

Outline of Lesson Plans

I. KNOWLEDGE

A. KNOWLEDGE OF GOD'S WORD: Study questions are given to help you apply God's Word to yourself and your situation.

B. KNOWLEDGE OF SELF: Self-evaluation is necessary in the light of God's authoritative commands. Assignments are given to help you make an accurate assessment.

II. WISDOM

A. WISDOM IN SELF-DISCIPLINE: Homework is given to enable you to improve your service to God as an elder.

B. WISDOM IN DISCIPLING OTHERS: Work is given which may help you lead the flock and multiply Christian growth in others.

Lesson One

YOUR CALLING

I Timothy 1
Also read II Timothy 1;
Titus 1:1-4; 10-16.

I. KNOWLEDGE

A. KNOWLEDGE OF THE WORD: Study questions

1. Your Identity (vv. 1-2)

a. *Your purpose*

> [1]Paul, an apostle of Christ Jesus by order of God
> our Savior and of Christ Jesus our hope,

Who are you? What is your calling in life? Do you know
your calling as Paul knew his? Have you been appointed
from eternity for eternal life? For the eldership? Do you
know Jesus as Savior and Lord in a daily way? How do you
know these things?

b. *Your fruit*

> ²to Timothy, a true child in the faith: Help, mercy and peace from God the Father and Christ Jesus our Lord.

Do you have spiritual children? Have you ever trained and instructed someone you've led to saving faith in Christ? Have you taught anyone in the congregation apart from teaching that you may have done in a Sunday school class?

2. Your Instruction (vv. 3-11)
   a. *Commandment*

> ³As I urged you when I was going to Macedonia, remain at Ephesus so that you may give orders to certain persons to stop teaching different doctrines,

Do you realize that you are to command in the name of the Lord? How is this a serious responsibility? In what ways do you command? Have you taught others to teach and command?

b. *Protection*

> [4]and stop paying attention to myths and endless genealogies that promote farfetched ideas rather than God's program which is furthered by faith.

Do you protect the flock? How? What are some false teachings that you have faced? Are there any "myths, genealogies and speculations" in your flock? Do you know what your people believe and read?

c. *Management,* v. 4

Do you have faith? Do you live by faith? That is, is the "administration" or running of your life by faith? In concrete specific terms, explain how to discover whether your flock lives this way.

d. *Purpose of commandments*

> [5]Now the aim of this authoritative instruction is love that comes from a clean heart, a good conscience, and genuine faith.

How do you produce love? How can you know if your flock has good spiritual-moral discernment? How do you handle hypocrites?

e. *Discipline*

> [6]Certain persons, by taking poor aim, have missed these things and have turned aside to empty discussion, [7]wanting to be teachers of the law but not understanding either the words they speak or those things that they insist upon with such assurance.

What have you done to bring back wandering sheep? How have you handled people who are both wrong and proud? How should you?

f. *Content of your commands*

> [8]Now we know that the law is good whenever a person uses it lawfully,

Do you use the law in your own life? How do you use the Bible? How do you use it in discipline?

g. *Recipients of the commandments*

> [9]aware of this, that the law was not laid down for the righteous but for the lawless and rebellious, for the ungodly and sinners, for the unholy and profane, for those who murder fathers and those who murder mothers, for murderers in general, [10]for the sexually immoral, homosexuals, kidnappers, liars, perjurers, and everything else that is opposed to the healthy teaching

Do you have contact with people like those listed here? Do you avoid them? How do you use the Word in witnessing to them?

h. *The commandments as gospel*

> [11]that was entrusted to me in the glorious good news from the blessed God.

Do you hold out the Word of God as "good news?" Do you rejoice in it? Are you faithfully bringing it to the "lawless and rebellious" inside and outside of the church?

3. Your Salvation (vv. 12-17)
   a. *Your strength*

   > [12]I thank Christ Jesus our Lord Who strengthened me, that He considered me trustworthy, appointing me for service, [13]although prior to this I was a blasphemer and persecutor and a violent person. Yet I was shown mercy because ignorantly I acted in unbelief, [14]and our Lord's grace overflowed with faith and love in Christ Jesus.

   How has God strengthened you for your calling to the ministry of eldership? How has God shown mercy to (literally "mercied") you? Can you point out the "overflowing" grace of God in your life? List some ways that the love and faith of Christ have grown in you. Why has God done all of this?

b. *Your sin*

> [15]The saying is trustworthy and deserves full accep-
> tance that "Christ Jesus came into the world to save
> sinners," of whom I am the worst.

How did you blaspheme, persecute, and act arrogantly?
Describe your ignorance of Jesus Christ. In what ways and
at what times do you still sense your unworthiness? Do you
have assurance of salvation?

c. *Your standard*

> ¹⁶Yet it was for this very reason that I was shown mercy so that by me, the worst of sinners, Jesus Christ might display His perfect patience as a pattern for those who are coming to believe on Him for eternal life.

How is your life an example to those who believe?

d. *Your song*

> ¹⁷Now to the King of eternity, incorruptible, invisible, the only God, be honor and glory forever and ever. Amen.

How often do you think about your salvation *in the above manner*? Does this produce praise and doxologies?

4. Your Responsibility (vv. 18-20)
   a. *Chain of command*

> 18This authoritative instruction I entrust to you, Timothy, my son, in agreement with the prophecies about you that led me to you, that by their encouragement you may fight the good fight,

What chain of command do you live under in your congregation? To whom are the elders responsible? The presbytery? The synod or assembly? What did the laying on of hands mean to you? To God?

   b. *Challenge of responsibility,* v. 18

Are you aware of life's spiritual battle? How does this affect you as an elder? How do you prepare for the battle?

c. *Combat weapons*

[19]retaining faith and a good conscience which some have thrust aside, thereby making shipwreck of their faith. [20]Hymenaeus and Alexander are among those to whom I refer; I have handed them over to Satan so that they may be taught by discipline not to blaspheme.

Do you live by faith or sight? How clear is your conscience, and how much ability to discern right and wrong in yourself and others do you have? What could happen to you if you were to be lazy?

B. KNOWLEDGE OF SELF: Evaluation
   1. Your Call. How did you determine that you were called to be an elder? How did the congregation? How did the presbytery? Were these decisions biblically based?

2. Your Preparation. What preparation did you make before you accepted the call? Did your congregation train you? Did the presbytery? If so, how? Was this preparation adequate?

3. Your Service. Since taking office, have you evaluated your service? How? How well have you served?

4. Your Identity. When someone asks you who you are and what you do, do you tell them you are God's child and elder, or do you speak only of your occupation? Is your occupation more important to you than your calling? Do you remember your ordination vows?

5. Read *The Elders of the Church,* L. R. Eyres, (Phillipsburg: Presbyterian and Reformed Pub. Co., 1975) or read *Unto Every Good Work: A Manual for Elders,* R. W. Nickerson, Ed. (Pittsburgh: Reformed Presbyterian Board of Education and Publication, 1974) third revised printing.

II. WISDOM

A. WISDOM IN SELF DISCIPLINE

1. Prayerfully decide whether or not you really *want* to take this course and face God's Word. This will mean putting off the old man and putting on the new, which entails effort and often pain. Make a covenant with God, once you realize what you are doing.

2. Make an initial evaluation of yourself as an elder. Make a list of all your strengths and weaknesses. *Be honest,* since this evaluation will be used as the base from which growth in grace will be measured. Rate yourself on a 5-high; 0-low scale.

B. WISDOM IN DISCIPLING OTHERS

1. Share the goals of this course with your wife. Show her your self-evaluation and ask her to change it where she disagrees. Offer to help her do the same with her life and responsibilities.

2. Each elder should evaluate the others on the eldership. Pair up as partners for prayer and work.

Lesson Two

YOUR PRAYER

I Timothy 2:1-8
Also read Titus 3:1-2.

I.   KNOWLEDGE

A. KNOWLEDGE OF THE WORD: Study Questions
  1. The Pattern of Prayer

> [1]First of all, then, I urge that requests, prayers, petitions and thanksgivings be made for all sorts of persons;

  a. *Urgency.* Do you recognize the urgency of prayer? Give examples.

b. *Definition*. Do you know what these different words mean?
  (1) Petition: Do you petition for specific things? What are some?
    (a) What is the purpose of petition? Jn. 14:13; 15:7, 8; Mt. 9:38; Lk. 10:2. God's glory.

    (b) What is the plan of petition? Jn. 14:14-15; 15:7-8; I Jn. 3:22; 5:14-15. According to God's will.

    (c) What is the power of petition? Heb. 5:7; Jn. 14:13-14; 15:15-16; 16:24, 26. The Name of Jesus, i.e., His person and work.

(2) Prayer: Do you pray to God?

   (a)   Do you ever just "cry out" to Him? Acts 2:21; 9:14; Rom. 10:13-14; I Cor. 1:2.

   (b)   Do you have an awareness of "bowing down in worship" when you pray? Phil. 2:10-11; Heb. 1:6; Rev. 4:10-11; 5:14; 7:11-12; 11:16-18; 14:7; 15:2-4; 22:9.

   (c)   Do you "praise" Him? Lk. 1:64; 2:28-32; Eph. 1:3; I Pet. 1:3.

   (d)   Do you "fellowship" with God? Mt. 6:5-15; Rom. 8:26-27; I Tim. 2:8.

(3) Entreaty: Do you "invoke" the Lord's blessings? Do you dedicate all things and persons to God and to His service? I Tim. 2:1; 4:5.

(4) Thanksgiving: Do you thank Him? Phil. 4:4; I Thess. 5:18.
   (a) Do you thank Him for Himself? II Chron. 6:14, 18-21. What amazes you about Him?

   (b) Do you thank Him for His acts of salvation? Which ones? Eph. 1:3, cf. 4-14.

(c) When do you thank Him? I Thess. 5:18. Do you have peace as a result of thankfulness? Phil. 4:7, 9; Col. 3:15.

c. *Regularity.* Do you pray regularly? When?

d. *Teaching.* Have you ever taught someone to pray? Who else did this? Lk. 11:1-4.

2. The Purpose of Prayer

> ²for kings and all who are in high positions, so that we may lead a peaceful and calm life in all godliness and seriousness. ³This is good and acceptable before God our Savior,

a. *Prayer concerns all men.* Do you pray for all kinds of people? Do you pray for public officials? Do you pray for men in authority in all of society? Do you *regularly* pray for our government?

b. *The purpose of prayer is tranquility.* Do you pray specifically for a quiet life? Why? Do you ask for ease or a lifestyle that will enable you to live with godliness and dignity? How would this tend to glorify God? Do you realize this pleases God? Do your blessings lead to godliness or laziness?

3. The Basis of Prayer

> ⁴Who wants all sorts of persons to be saved and to come to a full knowledge of the truth. ⁵There is one God and one Mediator between God and human beings (Himself a human being), Christ Jesus ⁶Who gave Himself as a ransom payment for all sorts of persons, a fact witnessed to at the right time,

a. *God is Savior.* How conscious are you that the orderliness of life is due to God's hand? In what ways has God been your Savior and Protector? Has He been gracious to you in a special way?

b. *Jesus Christ is the Mediator.* Do you come directly to God? What is a mediator? Why do you need one? Does this mediatorial work of Christ have anything to do with His gift of salvation? How is Jesus your Mediator *today?* Why is the humanity of Christ emphasized in connection with His mediatorial work? cf. Rom. 5:12-21; Heb. 2:14-18.

4. The Products of Prayer

> ⁶Who gave Himself as a ransom payment for all sorts of persons, a fact witnessed to at the right time, ⁷for which I was appointed a preacher and an apostle (I am speaking the truth; I am not lying), a teacher of the Gentiles in faith and truth. ⁸Therefore, in every place, I want men to pray without anger or arguing, lifting up holy hands.

  a. *Testimony.* What was Jesus Christ's witness? cf. I Tim. 6:13. What times do we live in? Why?

  b. *Proclamation.* Although Paul was an apostle, what does your call have in common with his? What is a herald? Do you publicly proclaim Jesus Christ?

c. *Earnestness.* Do you "hold up" holy hands? What does that mean? cf. Ex. 17:8-13. Do you wrestle with God as did Jacob (Gen. 32:24-32). Do you have a conscience free from condemnation? Do you have peace and openness with your Christian brothers?

B. KNOWLEDGE OF SELF
1. For two weeks keep a record of your prayer.
   a. Record *when* you pray and for *how long.*
   b. Record the *content* of your prayers.

Week One

Week Two

2. Analyze your prayer.
   a. Does it contain worship? Does it contain confession of general sins, and specific sins? Is there much pure praise? Is there fellowship with God?

   b. How much thanksgiving "salts" your prayer? Would you say you are thankful for everything?

   c. How common is the dedication of things, persons and time to your prayer?

d. What kinds of petitions do you make: Do they focus on God's kingdom? How often are they consistent with God's will as revealed in the Scriptures? Are they consciously presented through faith in the Name of Jesus Christ, i.e., His person and work?

e. Rate yourself in these four categories. Scale: 5-high; 0-low.

II. WISDOM

A. WISDOM IN SELF-DISCIPLINE

1. After completing your analysis for two weeks, outline your prayers. Correct your weaknesses so that your prayers will be more biblical, along the lines studied. Each day, before you pray, read Romans 8:26-39.

Week One

Week Two

2. Begin keeping a record of your petitions. Note the date and content of God's answers. Thank God for His answers.

B. WISDOM IN DISCIPLING OTHERS
   1. Share your month of prayer with your wife. Help her evaluate her prayer.
   2. Share your personal results with your partner on the elder board.
   3. Each elder team should share these things, if possible, on their next visit to someone in the congregation.

Lesson Three

YOUR RELATIONSHIP TO WOMEN

I Timothy 2:9-15

I. KNOWLEDGE
A. KNOWLEDGE OF THE WORD: Study Questions
1. Modesty

> [9]So too, women should beautify themselves in attractive clothing with modesty and moderation, not with braided hair or gold or pearls or costly clothing, [10]but with good deeds that match women who claim to be religious.

a. *Other women.* What kind of women do you notice? Do you appreciate modestly dressed, non-flirtatious women? Do you have problems with some who are not? How would you counsel and solve the problem of a woman who dressed immodestly in your flock? In your youth group?

b. *Your own.* Do you have the same dress standard for your wife and daughter as for other women? Do you help your family in this regard? Do you also help your wife and daughters in the area of good works? How do you cultivate these works in these women?

2. Instruction

> [11]Let a woman learn in silence with complete sub-missiveness. [12]I don't permit a woman to teach or to exercise authority over a man but to remain silent. [13]Adam was formed first, then Eve; [14]and Adam was not deceived, but the woman being entirely deceived fell into transgression. [15]But she will be saved through the childbearing, if they continue in faith and love and sanctification with good sense.

a. *Other women.* Do you instruct women in the church? Do any women exert authority over you? Why are churches in the USA often weak in character? Why do men "cop-out" on responsibilities? How are we helping our women to continue in faith, love and self-control? How have you taught women to disciple others?

b. *Your own.* Do you pray with and instruct your wife? Do you discipline her in the areas of faith, love, holiness and self-control? How? Do you help her face temptation? Have you worked out the ways in which your children ought to be raised? Do you help your wife in disciplining the children? Have you instructed your daughters about dating and marriage?

B. KNOWLEDGE OF SELF: Evaluation
　　1. Evaluate your relationship with women other than your wife.
　　　　a. Do you treat them as objects or persons? Do you evaluate
　　　　　　women on physical attractiveness or on other qualities? Do
　　　　　　you take notice and praise God for modesty? Do you strug-
　　　　　　gle with lust? Rate yourself on sexual purity.
　　　　　　Scale: 5-high; O-low.

　　　　b. Do you lead or drive women? Do you lead or demand? Are
　　　　　　you polite to women? Do you open doors, pull out chairs,
　　　　　　etc.? Are you patient with women? Do you see yourself as
　　　　　　superior to women? How?

2. Evaluate your relationship with your wife.
   a. Do you treat her as an object or a person? Do you love her as Christ loves the church? Eph. 5:22-33. Do you find your wife attractive? Do you tell her? How often? Do you spend time alone with her? Do you oversee your wife's clothing to ensure modesty? Do you meet your wife's sexual needs?

    b. Does your wife respect your leadership? Do you *really* understand her? Are you polite to her? Do you honor her as a fellow heir of grace? Are you patient with her or are your prayers hindered? I Pet. 3:7. Do you instruct her in the Word of God and pray with her other than at family worship? Do you communicate and share yourself with her? Are you solving problems in a loving manner? How? Rate your overall care and leadership on the 5-0 scale.

II. WISDOM
A. WISDOM IN SELF-DISCIPLINE
  1. If sexual lust is a problem, work out a system that will enable you to flee sexual temptations.
     Example: When tempted, follow these steps:
     a. First, pray for forgiveness immediately and briefly.
     b. Second, pray for the woman or girl. If she is modest, ask for her protection. If she is a true temptation, ask the Holy Spirit to convict her and protect righteous men from her.
     c. Third, immediately get involved in what you should be doing to please your God.
     d. Fourth, have your wife pray for this problem.

  2. List five *new* ways you can treat women with gentleness and respect so that you will see them as persons who are God's image-bearers and not objects.

3. Read *Christian Living in the Home,* Jay E. Adams, (Phillipsburg: Presbyterian and Reformed Pub. Co., 1972). Read the chapter "Loving Leadership" twice. Review your self-evaluation in regard to your marriage. Readjust your 5-0 scale and make a list of your sins and failures in the marriage. List five concrete ways in which you can improve. Next, list the problems in the marriage that need to be solved, together with possible solutions.

B. WISDOM IN DISCIPLING OTHERS

1. Teach a teenage boy or young adult how to overcome lustful thoughts and/or masturbation. Perhaps this can be done discreetly in a class of teenage boys in a general lesson.

2. Share your evaluation of your leadership in the marriage with your wife, asking for forgiveness where necessary and for help in planning and executing your desired changes towards godliness. Discuss *Christian Living in the Home* with your wife. Try to enlist her help on a regular basis. Perhaps she can aid you in your growth as an elder, once she aids you in the husband-wife relationship.

3. Mention your growth in this area on your pastoral visits. Make it a point to explain the changes, rather than just describing them. Use this as a teaching, discipling opportunity. Those elders that are particularly blessed should be "on call" to counsel other couples.

4. One or more elders should teach a seminar on married life, i.e., husband-wife relationships, whether in Sunday School, the Youth Group, or in Vacation Bible School.

Lesson Four

YOUR OFFICE

I Timothy 3
Also read Titus 1:5-9; Titus 3:3-8;
II Timothy 2:8-13.

I. KNOWLEDGE

A. KNOWLEDGE OF THE WORD: Study Questions

1. Your Office (vv. 1-7)

   a. *Reliability*

   > [1]The saying is trustworthy: "Whoever aspires to become an overseer desires to do a fine work."

   Do you trust this description? Do you ever *use* it in evaluating someone who is running for the office of elder? Have you ever used it in a self-evaluation?

b. *Readiness*, v. 1

Do you seek, i.e., "stretch" for the office? Do you like to manage or oversee things? Do you have a tendency to let things slide or do you see them through to the end? Do you like to shepherd others? Do you have a desire, i.e., passion, for the work? Do you see it as good, better than other callings?

c. *Requirements*

> [2]Therefore, an overseer must be beyond criticism, the husband of only one wife, level-headed, sensible, orderly, hospitable, teachable,

Is there any charge, legal or otherwise against you? Are you content with your wife? (See ch. 2:9-15.) Are you self-controlled with all things: food, drink, tobacco, TV, etc.? Do you think clearly? Do you make rash decisions? Do you have common sense and wisdom? Do people look up to you and respect you? Are you hospitable? Do you entertain strangers *in the congregation?* Do you entertain *total* strangers? Do you excel in hospitality, or are you just better than many others in the congregation (Rom. 12:13, Heb. 13:2)? Do you teach? Are you a model? Are you a *student* of the Word?

³not enslaved to wine, not a fighter, but lenient, uncontentious, not after money.

Are you addicted to wine or any drugs? Are you an "ornery cuss"? Do you like to argue? Are you gentle? Peaceful? Do you fit Matthew 5:9? Do you love money? Are you generous with it? Do you tithe? Do you give more than the tithe?

⁴He must manage his own household well, keeping his children in subjection with complete dignity

Do you "stand at the head" of your house? Do you take leadership? Do things run smoothly or loosely at home—e.g., are people on time, are the chores done, is time used wisely, are you in control of TV, etc.? Are your children "under order," i.e., are they controlled? With dignity?

⁵(if someone doesn't know how to manage his own
household, how can he care for God's church?),

Do you see how the congregation is to be managed as a
family? Do you do this? Do you qualify as an elder in this
respect?

⁶not a new convert, lest becoming inflated with pride
he might fall into the judgment of the devil.

When did you become a Christian? How long after this did
you become an elder? Does your position ever give you
cause for sinful pride? For conceit? Do you know how to
handle responsibility and authority?

> [7]He also must have a fine reputation among outsiders lest he fall into disgrace and into the devil's trap.

What do non-Christian relatives, neighbors and co-workers think of you? Do you realize that you are an elder in front of the watching world? What is testimony by action? Do you guard it?

2. Your helpers: Deacons (vv. 8-13)
   a. *Requirements*

   > [8]Deacons too must be serious, not double-tongued, not dependent upon much wine, not willing to accept dishonest gain,

   Are your deacons dignified? Are they men of their word? Are they honest and accurate? Are they given to wine? Drugs? Are they men who like to take advantage of others, i.e., outsmart others, dishonestly to take advantage of them?

⁹holding the secret of the faith with a clean conscience.

Do they understand God's historical plan of salvation? Do they have clear consciences?

¹²Deacons must be husbands of only one wife, who manage their children and their own households well.

Do the deacons have problems with women? Are their houses in order? Well run? Exemplary?

¹³Now those who serve well as deacons acquire a respected position for themselves and much boldness in the faith that is in Christ Jesus.

Are they confident in the faith? Do they have assurance? Are they bold in their witness? Do they serve? Do they want to?

¹¹The women too must be serious, not slanderers, level-headed, faithful in everything.

What about the women who help the deacons? Are they dignified? Are they slanderous gossips? Self-controlled? Dependable and faithful?

b. *Rating*

> [10]Moreover, they must be tested first, then if they are free from all suspicion, let them serve.

Did you evaluate deacons and candidates on these traits? Do you really know them, i.e., as deacons? Are they your disciples? Were they tested? Evaluated? Do you direct them? How can you help them do the work of a deacon more effectively?

3. Your godliness, vv. 15-16.
   a. *Your congregation*

   > ¹⁵but if I am delayed, you will know by them how you must behave in God's house, which is the church of the living God, as a pillar and support of the trust.

   Is it the household of God? Does it function like a smoothly running home? Is there real familial *love* in it? Does God the Holy Spirit walk among you? Do you uphold the truth? The whole truth?

   b. *Your confession*

   > ¹⁶Admittedly great, indeed, is the secret of godliness that "He appeared in flesh, was vindicated in spirit, was seen by angels, was preached among the nations, was trusted in the world, was taken up in glory."

   Do you believe your confession? Do your members hold to the *Westminster Confession of Faith* (or other standards)?

B. KNOWLEDGE OF SELF: Evaluation
   1. According to each individual requirement, both positive and negative, rate yourself, using the 5-0 scale.
   2. Have your wife evaluate you.
   3. Have the other elders evaluate you.
   4. Have your employer or employee rate you.

II. WISDOM
A. WISDOM IN SELF-DISCIPLINE
    1. Eldership
        a. List 5 specific and concrete ways to improve in your weak areas.
        b. Ask other elders who are strong in your weak areas to help you. Also enlist their prayers.
        c. Ask your wife's help in implementing these new ways of serving the Lord.

    2. Deacons
        a. Ask the deacons about their needs and problems.
        b. As elders, develop ways to help the deacons, and to use them more effectively.

B. WISDOM IN DISCIPLING OTHERS
1. Eldership
   a. Help the other elders to improve in your strengths.

   b. Help a young man aspiring to the eldership to evaluate his gifts and develop them along the above lines. Take him with you on several kinds of visits and train him to call and counsel.

   c. Share your evaluation of your office and your growth with at least one elder at presbytery and/or with an elder of a congregation outside of your denomination. Be prepared to mention this course with his elders or board.

2. Deacons
   a. Work out a training program for the deacons using this program as a model. Be sure to include provisions for the deacons to disciple others in the congregation.

Lesson Five

YOUR CHALLENGE

I Timothy 4
Also read II Timothy 2:14-3:9,
Titus 3:9-11.

I. KNOWLEDGE

A. KNOWLEDGE OF THE WORD: Study Questions
1. Your times and their challenge (vv. 1-5)
   a. *The challenge*

   > [1]Now here are the words that the Spirit speaks plainly: that in times later on some will turn away from the faith by paying attention to deceiving spirits and teachings of demons, [2]through the hypocrisy of liars whose consciences have become as desensitized as if they were seared by a hot iron. [3]They forbid people to marry and require abstinence from certain foods...

   What are the last times? When were they to begin? When will they end? Can we work out a timetable? What kind of teaching characterizes this time? Who promotes this kind of teaching? What is the basic lie in this type of teaching? How aware are you of the last times? How aware are you of demonic teaching? Have you met people with seared consciences?

b. *The answer*

> …that God created to be shared with thanksgiving
> by those who believe and fully know the truth.
> ⁴Everything created by God is good, and nothing is
> to be rejected if it is received with thanksgiving,
> ⁵since it is sanctified by God's Word and prayer.

Can you name one thing that God created as evil? If everything is good, and we use it gratefully, why can't we have
everything? What are the two elements in sanctifying
something to God? What does "by God's Word" mean?
How often do you use the Bible to find out *how* to use
something in God's world? Do you dedicate things, actions
and persons to God? How often?

2. Your Answer to the Times and Discipline (vv. 6-16)
    a. *The challenge*

    What effects do demonic teachings have? What happens to older women? What kinds of stories do they tell? How? How does this work itself out in a devastating way in a nursing or convalescent home? Why is non-reality so harmful?

    b. *The answer*

    (1) Is found in God's Word, the Bible, v. 6

    ⁶If you advise the brothers about these things you will be a good servant of Christ Jesus, nourished by the words of the faith and of the good teaching that you have followed closely.

    What is the answer to these demonic tales? How does the Word help here?

(2) Discipline

> [7]But avoid godless and old-womanish myths, and discipline yourself for godliness; [8]Bodily exercise has limited value, but godliness is of unlimited value, holding promise for the present life and the life to come. [9]The saying is trustworthy and deserves full acceptance: [10]"We labor and struggle for this goal because we have set our hope on a living God," Who is the Savior of all sorts of men, especially of those who believe.

How disciplined are you in prayer and Bible reading? Have you grown more like Jesus Christ over the last year? Can you measure your growth?

(3) Your example

> [11]Instruct and teach these things with authority. [12]Don't let anybody despise your youth; rather, become a model for believers in speech, in behavior, in love, in faithfulness and in purity. [13]Until I come pay attention to the public reading of Scripture, to exhortation, to teaching. [14]Don't neglect the gift that is in you, that was given to you by means of prophecy when the members of the presbytery laid their hands on you. [15]Practice these things; be fully involved in them so that your progress may be apparent to everybody. [16]Pay attention to yourself and to your teaching. Continue in these things; by doing so you will save both yourself and those who hear you.

How does this growth affect your role as teacher or model? Can people imitate your words, behavior, sacrificial love, faithfulness and purity? How much time do you give to the public reading of the Word? To exhortation? To teaching? Is your calling as an elder *central* to your life? Test yourself in how much attention you give to these duties. Do you remain steady in them, or do you fluctuate up and down? Do you see progress in your own life? Do others? Are you a disciplined person in general?

c. For one week, carefully study the newspapers or a news magazine listing the types of demonic teaching you find. Also note the results of these non-biblical teachings.

B. KNOWLEDGE OF SELF: Evaluation
   1. Make a time study for two weeks. Write down *everything* that you do, and when you start and stop. Total each activity for each week. This will enable you to see how you use your time. Check to see if you spend more time doing wasteful or unnecessary things than you spend praying and studying the Bible. Make a particular note of the work you do as an elder.

Week One

Week Two

2. Ask your wife and a non-relative to rate you on your *example* in the five areas of verse 12, using the 5-0 scale.

II. WISDOM

A. WISDOM IN SELF-DISCIPLINE

1 Read pp. 281-2, 338-43 in *The Christian Counselor's Manual,* J.E. Adams (Grand Rapids: Zondervan, 1973), on scheduling.

2. Using the worksheet for scheduling on p. 340, work on your schedule.

3. Review *Christian Living in the Home* to help with biblical priorities. The suggested order is: personal worship, wife, children, eldership, vocation, etc.

4. Review your work on Lesson Two to ensure disciplined prayer.

Scheduling

B. WISDOM IN DISCIPLING OTHERS

1. Help one person in your family to schedule his time and personal worship.
2. Impart your learning during your visits as an elder to members of the flock.
3. Teach one person outside your home to schedule his life.

Lesson Six

YOUR MANAGEMENT
OF GOD'S HOUSEHOLD

I Timothy 5:1-6:10,17-19
Also read Titus 2.

I. KNOWLEDGE

A. KNOWLEDGE OF THE WORD: Study Questions

1. Overseeing Relationships in the Household of God (vv. 1-2)

> [1]Don't sharply rebuke an older man but appeal to him as if he were your father; deal with younger men as brothers, [2]older women as mothers, younger women as sisters, with absolute purity.

a. *Older people*

Do you treat older people as you treat other people? Do you speak respectfully to them? Do you seek their advice? Do you remember their important days, e.g., birthdays, anniversaries, etc.? Do you meet their physical, social and spiritual needs? Are you patient with them? How does the congregation rate you on these matters?

b. *Younger people*

Do you treat younger people as brothers and sisters? Do you spend time with them and teach them things? Do you take them places? Do you remember their special days? Do they respect you and seek your advice? How does the congregation rate you on these matters?

2. Overseeing the Needs in the Household (vv. 3-16)
    a. *Widows*

> ³Honor widows who really are widows.

Do you have ways of determining needs? Do you know the needs of widows in the congregation? Do you know the needs of others? Does the congregation know and care about needy people in the church? How about those outside of it?

> ⁵Now the one who is really a widow, and has been left all alone, has set her hope on God and continues making requests and prays night and day, ⁶but the one who lives wastefully is dead while she lives. ⁷So, give these authoritative instructions that they may be beyond reproach.

How do you evaluate the godliness of a widow? What does it mean to fix one's hope on God? Does she do nothing *but* pray? How does she differ from the "merry widow" of verse 6? Can you give an example of each type? Have you ever confronted a widow or widower on this account?

b. *Care of widows*
   (1) Family

> ⁴But if any widow has children or grandchildren, let them learn to practice their religious duty to their own household first, and repay something to their parents; this is acceptable in God's sight.... ⁸But whoever does not provide for his own, and especially for the members of his own household, has denied the faith and is worse than an unbeliever.

> Do you care for your own relatives? Are the second and third generations of the congregation meeting the physical, social and spiritual needs of their parents and/or grandparents? Do the families of the congregation give evidence of biblical love across generations? Have you ever discipled anyone because of his failure to help his parents in *any* of the above ways?

(2) Friends

> [16]If any believing woman has widows in her family, let her give them relief, so that the church may not be burdened and may relieve those who really are widows.

Have you seen the need for "adopting" older folks? What care do you give to these people? Have you taken any into your home? Does the congregation see the deacons' fund as a tool for evangelism? Do they understand that the fund goes farther if families take care of their own members?

(3) Congregation

Do you care for your own? Does the state do a better job? Does the congregation see its potential and obligation? What have you done to teach them these biblical values?

c. *Use of Widows*

> [9]Enroll a widow only if she is not less than sixty years old, was the wife of only one husband, [10]has a reputation for good works, if she has brought up children, if she has been hospitable to strangers, if she has washed the feet of saints, if she has relieved the afflicted, if she pursued every sort of good work. [11]But don't include younger widows; when they experience sensual desires they want to marry and thereby break their commitment to Christ, [12]and become guilty of setting aside their first pledge of faith. [13]Besides, they learn to be idle persons, making the rounds of people's houses, and not only idle persons, but also gossips and busybodies speaking things that they ought not. [14]I want younger widows, then, to marry, to have children, to run their homes, and give the opponent no opportunity for insult. [15]Already some have turned aside to follow Satan.

(1) Older widows. Do you have a list of older widows who meet these qualifications? Do you utilize their efforts in helping younger women and children? In other work for the Lord?

(2) Younger widows. Do you make sure younger widows (also singles, divorcees, those separated or those left alone while husbands are at work) are not lazy? Do you know the lifestyles of younger women? In general, do you encourage women to center their lives around their husbands, to do good deeds, to raise children, to show hospitality, to serve others and aid those in trouble? Do you encourage young widows (and divorcees where proper) to remarry? Have you ever helped a woman to find a husband? Have you ever counseled a young couple before marriage? Can you give examples of women who were going to "serve the Lord" but got sidetracked? Have you seen this happen in men? Is your congregation *holy?* Is there a lot of "setting aside the first pledge"? Do you see a lack of *consistent* service?

3. Overseeing Overseers, vv. 17-25

> [17]The elders who manage well should be considered worthy of double pay, especially those who are laboring at preaching and teaching. [18]The Scripture says, "Don't muzzle the ox while he is treading out the grain," and "The worker is worthy of his wages." [19]Don't receive a charge against an elder unless it is supported by two or three witnesses. [20]Those who go on sinning convict in the presence of all, so that the rest may fear. [21]In the presence of God and Christ Jesus and the chosen angels I solemnly call on you to observe these things without prejudice, doing nothing out of favoritism. [22]Don't lay hands on anybody hastily; don't share in the sins of others. Keep yourself pure. [23](Don't drink only water from now on; rather use a little wine because of your stomach and your frequent ailments.) [24]The sins of some people are evident, directing you to your judgment of them, but the sins of others follow later. [25]So too good deeds are evident beforehand, and even those that aren't cannot remain hidden.

a. *Elders*

Does the congregation honor their elders? Do you rule well? Are you worthy of double honor (also financially)? Do you teach? Do you toil and labor over the Word? Do you refuse to gossip about another elder? Do you refuse to hear charges unless verified biblically? Do you rebuke public sins publicly? Do you care for your body?

b. *Future elders*

Have you placed hands on people? Can you honestly say whether or not it was too quickly? Do you test your candidates? How? Do you know how to detect sins in candidates that would disqualify them?

4. Overseeing the callings of the household's members (6:1-2)

> [1]All who are under the yoke of slavery must regard their lords worthy of full respect lest the Name of God and the teaching be blasphemed. [2]Those who have believing lords must not show any less respect because they are brothers, but on the contrary they must serve all the better because those who benefit from their good service are believers and dear friends. Teach and urge these things.

Do you know if your sheep give their Christian employers respect and full effort? Do they honor their non-Christian bosses? Do your people work for the Lord? Do their bosses and co-workers speak well of them? Do you help people to find their callings? Do you help them to get jobs? Do you help them to solve problems at work?

5. Overseeing the use of money in the family (6:3-10, 17-19)
   a. *The love of money*

> ³Whoever teaches differently and doesn't agree with the wholesome words of our Lord Jesus Christ and the teaching that is in keeping with godliness ⁴is conceited, understands nothing. He has an unhealthy desire for discussions and controversies over words, from which come envy, strife, blasphemies, suspicions, evils, ⁵incessant wranglings by persons with corrupted minds who are deprived of the truth, thinking about godliness in terms of gain. ⁶Of course, there is great gain in godliness linked with contentment; ⁷after all, we brought nothing into the world, and we can't carry anything out of it. ⁸When we have food and clothing we shall be satisfied with these; ⁹but those who determine to be rich fall into temptation and a trap and into many foolish and injurious desires that plunge people into ruin and destruction. ¹⁰The love of money is a root of all sorts of evils. Some, eager for money, have wandered away from the faith and have pierced themselves through with many sorrows.

Do you love money? Do you love material things? Security? Do you see the position of elder as a means of financial gain? Are you content to be godly? Has your desire for material things ever gotten you into trouble? Have you ever found your zeal for God's face erased by material things? Do you watch for this in calls on your people? Have you ever seen anyone destroyed in this way?

b. *The use of money*

> [17]Authoritatively instruct the rich of this present age not to be haughty, nor to set their hope on the uncertainty of riches, but rather on God, Who richly provides everything for our enjoyment. [18]They must do good, be rich in good deeds, be ready to give, generous, [19]laying up the treasure of a good foundation for the future so that they may lay hold on the life that is really life.

Do you put your hope in doing good? Are you rich in good deeds? Are you generous with your money and goods? Do you put more effort into obtaining life insurance or eternal life? Do you instruct the wealthy in the congregation to use their money for the Lord? Do you ensure their building up an eternal foundation?

B. KNOWLEDGE OF SELF: Evaluation
   1. At an elders' meeting, rate yourselves (as a board) in management of the five areas of oversight. Use the 5-0 scale.
   2. Make notes of specific failures to use biblical methods of managing God's household. Also note failures to maintain biblical standards in your household.
   3. Ask the eldership or board of a well-managed church to evaluate your management as spelled out in numbers 1 and 2 of this section.

II. WISDOM
A. WISDOM IN SELF-DISCIPLINE
1. Read *Body Life,* R. Steadman (Grand Rapids: Discovery House Pub., 1995).
2. Look over *The Ministry of Management,* National Conference on Church Management (Arrowhead Springs, San Bernardino, California: Campus Crusade for Christ).
3. Have several meetings to develop specific, concrete ways of teaching members to act as a family, to meet the needs of others, to respect their leaders, to work at their callings and to use money biblically in *your* congregation.
4. Read *Shepherding God's Flock,* Part III, Jay E. Adams (Grand Rapids: Zondervan, 1975). Develop overall goals for the congregation and biblical methods to achieve them.
5. Set specific dates for periodic evaluations and planning sessions.

B. WISDOM IN DISCIPLING OTHERS
1. Teach the deacons to plan and manage their work.
2. Teach the board of elders of a sister congregation how to evaluate and manage their congregation.

Lesson Seven

YOUR DISCIPLING

Eph. 4:1-16; II Tim. 2:1-7

I. KNOWLEDGE

A. KNOWLEDGE OF THE WORD: Study Questions

1. Eph. 4:1-16.

[1]So then, as a prisoner for the Lord, I urge you to walk in a way that is appropriate to the calling to which you were called, [2]with complete humility and meekness, with patience putting up with one another in love, [3]doing your best to keep the unity of the Spirit by the bond of peace. [4]There is one body and one Spirit, just as when you were called there is one hope to which you were called. [5]There is one Lord, one faith, one baptism, [6]one God and Father of all, Who is over all and through all, and in all.

[7]Now grace was given to each one of us according to the measure that Christ determined. [8]That is why it says, Having ascended to the heights, He led His captives into captivity and gave gifts to the people. [9](Now, "Having ascended"—what meaning does this have unless He also had descended into the lower parts of the earth? [10]He Who descended is the same One Who also ascended far above all the heavens, that He might fill all things.) [11]He gave some as apostles, some as prophets, some as evangelists and some as shepherds and teachers, [12]to equip the saints for a work of service leading to the building up of Christ's body [13]until we all attain to the unity of the faith and to the full knowledge of God's Son, to mature manhood, to the point where we become as fully adult as Christ. [14]This must happen so that we may no longer be infants, blown about and carried around by every wind of teaching, by human trickery, by craftiness designed to lead to error. [15]But by speaking the truth in love we may grow up in all respects into Him Who is the Head, that is, Christ, [16]from Whom the whole body fitted together and harmoniously joined together by every joint that is provided, in keeping with the proportion of effort contributed by each individual part, brings about the growth of the body so as to build itself up by love.

Who is the unifying agent in the church? How do individuals get different gifts? What are some of the gifts that God gives (Rom. 12:3-8; I Cor. 12:1-31)? How does Christ build the church, as a "building" (Eph. 2:20)? What were the apostles and prophets (Eph. 2:20)? What are the pastors-teachers to the church? What do the pastors do as their *major* task? How do they train and equip the body? Do you do this? How? Is your congregation mature? Have you helped or hindered this growth? Have you equipped each individual part to work properly so as to supply what it should?

6

2. II Timothy 2:1-7

> [1]You, then, my child, find strength in the help that Jesus Christ gives. [2]And the things that you heard from me before many witnesses pass along to trustworthy persons who will be competent to teach others also. [3]Endure your share of suffering as a good soldier of Christ Jesus. [4]A soldier avoids becoming involved in everyday business activities so that he may please the one who enlisted him. [5]Again, an athlete isn't awarded the winner's wreath unless he competes according to the rules. [6]It is the laboring farmer who deserves to have the first share of the crops. [7]Consider what I am saying; the Lord will give you understanding in all things.

What is the power that enables sinful men to pastor others? Are you "strong in God's grace"? Do you see teaching others to teach as a major task of the eldership? Do you disciple others? Is there a discipling program in the congregation? Is the ability to disciple others a major goal in your eldership's prayer and planning? Do you have a leadership program as a phase of the congregation's discipling program? Do you realize that training others is a battle? Do you believe that it is a *necessary* part of your office? Do you realize that God will give you insight if you ask? How?

B. KNOWLEDGE OF SELF: Evaluation
   1. Do you understand the concept of discipling?

   2. How did Jesus teach and make disciples? Do you do this?

   3. Do you understand the great commission to make disciples? Rate your witnessing on the 5-0 scale.

   4. What is a disciple? Have you ever discipled anyone?

   5. Who teaches disciples today?

   6. How does He teach? By what methods?

7. What was Paul's method of teaching Timothy?

8. How did Timothy, in turn, teach others?

9. How does your teaching rate in following this biblical method? Use the 5-0 scale.

10. How does the overall teaching of the congregation rate? Does this place any obligation upon you as a teacher?

11. Do you disciple people or do you lecture them? Does anyone else do this?

12. Is the preaching, Sunday School teaching, youth work, etc., geared toward discipleship? What kinds of preparation do the teachers make?

13. Do you and they include the full life, teacher-disciple relationship that the Bible pictures for it? Do you aim for converts or disciples?

II. WISDOM
A. WISDOM IN SELF-DISCIPLINE
1. Using a concordance make a study of the words: teacher, teaching, doctrine, disciple, discipline, and other related words. Learn God's method in the teacher-disciple relationship.

   a. *Teacher*:

   b. *Teaching*:

   c. *Doctrine*:

c. *Disciple*:

d. *Discipline*:

e. *Other*:

2. Read "Christian School Teachers as Nouthetic Counselors," *Competent to Counsel,* Jay E. Adams (Grand Rapids: Zondervan, 1970).
3. Ask someone who is strong in your weak areas to disciple you.
4. Develop a discipling program that you can use to disciple others in living the Christian life.
5. Start to disciple your wife and children.
6. Disciple one other person who is under your pastoral care, e.g., in a Sunday School class, youth group, etc.
7. Write out results of these six items as you pursue them, adding as you go along.

B. WISDOM IN DISCIPLING OTHERS

1. Incorporate your new biblical data on discipleship into the program with the deacons started under Lesson Four, sec. II B-2.
2. Evaluate their progress in discipling others.
3. Develop and institute a structured discipling program to meet the needs of your congregation. Be sure it utilizes the talents and abilities of the members. Look for specific discipling from congregational "experts" in all areas, e.g., Bible study, use of the Scriptures in daily life, prayer, witnessing, ministry to the needy, encouragement, husband-wife relationships, family living, dating, education, vocations, witnessing, use of money, use of time, etc. Review Lesson Six, sec. II-A, and incorporate biblical discipling into your proposed plans.
4. Make a *special provision* in the overall discipling program to fulfill II Timothy 2:2. Develop methods for evaluating, choosing and training potential leaders for positions in the congregation, e.g., elders, deacons, Sunday School teachers and youth leaders.

Work space

Work space

Lesson Eight

YOUR WISDOM

II Timothy 3:10-17

I. KNOWLEDGE

A. KNOWLEDGE OF THE WORD: Study Questions

> [10]You, in contrast, as my disciple, have closely fol-lowed my teaching, my way of life, my purpose, my faith, my patience, my love, my endurance, [11]my persecutions, and the sufferings that I underwent at Antioch, at Iconium and at Lystra, what persecutions I bore. But the Lord rescued me from all of them. [12]In fact, all who want to live a godly life for Christ Jesus will be persecuted. [13]Evil persons and imposters will go on to their worst, deceiving and being deceived.
>
> [14]You, however, must continue in those things that you learned and are convinced of, knowing from whom you learned them, [15]and that from childhood you have known the sacred Scriptures, that are able to make you wise about salvation through faith in Christ Jesus. [16]All Scripture is breathed out by God and useful for teaching, for conviction, for correction and for disciplined training in righteousness, [17]in order to completely fit and fully equip the man from God for every good task.

1. Was Timothy Paul's disciple? How do you know? In what areas did he imitate Paul? Why did Paul suffer? Do you see the spiritual battle that is going on? Give examples. Do you suffer persecution?

2. How did you come to know Jesus Christ? What part did the Bible play? Can you remember the Scriptures that God used in your regeneration and conversion? Can you show a person, from the Bible, "the wisdom that leads to salvation"? Can you do this from the Old Testament exclusively? Can you show that faith in Jesus Christ, His atoning work on the cross, and His resurrection from the dead are the heart of the New Testament?

3. Do you believe that the Bible is the inspired, God-breathed, inerrant and therefore infallible Word of God? Does God speak *to you* in the Bible? How? What have you learned from the Bible? Give personal examples of how the Bible brought conviction to your heart. Give examples of how the Bible has corrected and restored a mess that you made. How has the Bible trained you?

4. How capable are you of solving problems biblically? Can you explain biblically the definition of husband-wife, parent-child and employer-employee relationships? Can you explain *how* they are to work? Can you help restore a broken relationship? Can you train others in maintaining the newly formed relationship? Can you counsel others biblically about worry, depression, lust, bitterness, fear, etc.? Is there any problem that the Bible does not answer? Do you *know* there are biblical answers for problems with which you have not dealt?

B. KNOWLEDGE OF SELF: Evaluation
1. Personal Use. How often do you read your Bible? Have you memorized Scripture verses? Do you still do this? Rate yourself on the use of the Bible as a personal means of grace. Use the 5-0 scale. How well can you use the Bible to define and solve your problems? Rate yourself.

2. Use of the Bible with Others. How well can you use the Bible to counsel others about salvation? Rate yourself.

II. WISDOM
A. WISDOM IN SELF-DISCIPLINE
  1. Personal.
      a. Develop a system for studying the Bible. Develop an ability to do both inductive (specific passage to general principles) book studies and deductive (general topics to specific applications to present need) topical studies.
      b. Keep a record of your findings from the Scriptures and your applications to daily living.

      c. Develop a system of references and teachings that relate to specific, concrete problems in people's lives. See "The Use of Scriptures in Counseling" in *Lectures on Counseling,* Jay E. Adams (Grand Rapids: Zondervan Pub. Co., 1975).
      d. Record when and how God has used these passages in your life and in the lives of others.

2. Using the Word with Others
   a. Read *Christ and Your Problems,*[1] *What do You do When you Worry all the Time*[1] and *Godliness through Discipline.*[1] As an elder board, discuss how the Scriptures are related to personal problems.
   b. After the first discussion, read *Competent to Counsel*[2] and *The Christian Counselor's Manual.*[2] Discuss the whole approach to using the Bible to solve sinful problems.
   c. Using *The Christian Counselor's Manual* as a guide, work through *The Christian Counselor's Casebook.*[2]
   d. Ruling elders should sit in with the pastor to observe how counseling from God's Word may be done. The pastor should let elders do some of the counseling. If training is needed, contact: the Institute for Biblical Counseling and Discipleship, 5333 Lake Murray Blvd., La Mesa, CA 91942.
      ibcdsdg@k-online.com, www.ibcd.org

   e. Read *Shepherding God's Flock,*[2] Part 1, to see how the relationship between the teaching elders and ruling elders should work.

---

[1] Jay E. Adams (Phillipsburg: Presbyterian and Reformed).
[2] Jay E. Adams (Grand Rapids: Zondervan)

B. WISDOM IN DISCIPLING OTHERS
  1. Teach your family how to study and use the Scriptures.
  2. Teach individuals how to do these two things for themselves and how to help others do so. Do this on your calls and elsewhere when opportunities arise.
  3. Teach those who have teaching positions, e.g., in Sunday School, in Christian schools and in youth groups, how to use the Scriptures in their lives and how to apply them to the lives of their students.

Lesson Nine

YOUR CHARGE

I Timothy 6:11-16, 20-21
Also read II Tim. 4; Titus 3:12-15.

I. KNOWLEDGE

A. KNOWLEDGE OF THE WORD: Study Questions

> [11] But you, man of God, flee these things; pursue righteousness, godliness, faithfulness, love, endurance, meekness. [12] Fight the gallant fight of faith. Lay hold on eternal life to which you were called when you made your fine confession in the presence of many witnesses. [13] I instruct you with authority in the presence of God, Who gives life to all things, and Christ Jesus, Who made the good confession when testifying before Pontius Pilate, [14] to keep the commandment unspotted and free from suspicion until the appearance of our Lord Jesus Christ, [15] which in His own time will be publicly displayed by the blessed and only Sovereign, the King of kings and Lord of lords, [16] the only One Who has death-lessness, Who dwells in unapproachable light, Whom no person has ever seen or can see, to Whom be honor and eternal might! Amen.

> [20] Timothy, guard that which was entrusted to you, turning away from the irreligious chatter and contradictions of what is falsely labeled "knowledge," [21] which some have professed but by taking poor aim have missed the target of the faith. May help be with you.

1. Do you see that you must flee the old sin of your life as you would a wild bear? Do you see that you must pursue what is holy as a hunter would his prey?

2. Do you "agonize" as an athlete would in a wrestling match?
    Do you comprehend the need to "latch on" to eternal life as a
    wrestler holds on to his opponent?

3. II Timothy 4:1, 2, 8

    > [1]In the presence of God and of Jesus Christ, Who is
    > going to judge the living and the dead, and by His
    > appearing and His empire, I solemnly call on you to
    > [2]preach the Word, be at it in season and out of sea-
    > son. Convict, reprove, urge with complete patience
    > and full teaching.

    Do you realize that this charge given to Timothy over 1900
    years ago is also *your* charge?

⁸What is left for me is the winner's wreath of righteousness lying at a distance, that the Lord (Who is the righteous Judge) will award to me on that Day; and not to me alone, but also to all those who have loved His appearing.

Above all, do you perceive that this charge is given to you in the presence of the absolutely holy and all powerful King? What are you doing to "safeguard" the "deposit" entrusted to you? Do you realize the reward?

B. KNOWLEDGE OF SELF: Evaluation
   1. Re-read the passages studied in this lesson.
   2. Plead for God the Holy Spirit to enable you to honestly take up the charge where you have failed and to discipline yourself to be vigilant in your calling.
   3. Rate yourself as to your fidelity to your calling on the 5-0 scale.

II. WISDOM
  A. WISDOM IN SELF-DISCIPLINE
    1. Set up a system of periodic self-evaluation
    2. Have your wife evaluate you in between.
    3. Have regular elder prayer meetings. Include self-evaluations as stated in Lesson Six, sec. II A-5 and Lesson Seven, sec. II B-3 and 4.
    4. Develop a basic presentation of the gospel based upon Scripture. Memorize the heart of these passages. In the future, develop variations for specific types of persons, e.g., Jehovah's Witnesses, Mormons, pleasure seekers, etc. Pray that God would give you many opportunities to call men to discipleship and make you a soul winner and discipler so that you may obey the command in II Timothy 4:5—"do the work of an evangelist, carry out your service to the full."

B. WISDOM IN DISCIPLING OTHERS
1. Fellowship with and exhort other elder boards.
2. Share this study and the results with the new men coming onto the board.
3. Share this in the presbytery and/or general assembly or synod.